ONE, TWO, BUCKLE MY SHOE…
Magical number rhymes, old and new

Liz Miles and Sara Wilkinson

Illustrated by Claire Mumford

AWARD PUBLICATIONS LIMITED

ISBN 1-84135-403-1

Copyright © 2006 Award Publications Limited

First published 2006

Published by Award Publications Limited
The Old Riding School,
Welbeck Estate,
Worksop,
Nottinghamshire S80 3LR

Printed in Malaysia

Original rhymes: *Four giants racing*, *How many fairies can you see?* and *Puff!* by
Liz Miles; *Fairy Blue*, *Fishing for hats* and *Five giant toes* by Sara Wilkinson.
Designed by Melissa Orrom Swan

Contents

Fairy Blue

Fairy Blue, Fairy Blue,
has a new shoe,
Fairy Blue has another one, too.
Two new shoes for Fairy Blue,
How many shoes are there on you?

Diddle, diddle, dumpling

Diddle, diddle, dumpling, my son John,
Went to bed with his trousers on;
One shoe off, and one shoe on,
Diddle, diddle, dumpling, my son John.

One, two, three, four, five

One, two, three, four, five,
Once I caught a fish alive.
Six, seven, eight, nine, ten,
Then I let it go again.

Why did you let it go?
Because it bit my finger so.
Which finger did it bite?
This little finger on the right.

Five fat sausages

Five fat sausages
sizzling in a pan,
Four turned brown, but one went BANG!

Four fat sausages
sizzling in a pan,
Three looked delicious, but one went

BANG!

Three fat sausages
sizzling in a pan,
Two turned crispy, but one went

BANG!

Two fat sausages
sizzling in a pan,
One fried nicely, but the other went

BANG!

One fat sausage
sizzling in a pan,
Cooked too much – and then went

BANG!

One giant went to mow

One giant went to mow,
Went to mow his meadow.
But he tripped on a hoe,
And stubbed his toe,
Oh, what a clumsy fellow!

Rub-a-dub-dub

Rub-a-dub-dub
Three trolls in a tub
And why do you think they are there?
Greasy, grimy, grubby and slimy,
They need a good scrub,
Before going off to the fair!

One, two, fairies look at you

One, two,
fairies look at you,

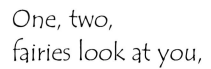

Two, three,
elves are drinking tea,

Three, four,
dragons shaking claws,

Four, five,
mermaids learn to dive.

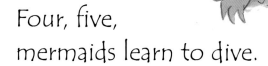

Five, six,
fairy wands and sticks,

Six, seven,
pixies live in Devon,

Seven, eight,
giants stay up late,

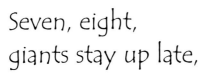

Eight, nine,
unicorns that dine,

Nine, ten,
little elvish men.

Five currant buns

Five currant buns in a baker's shop,
Shiny and round with a cherry on top.
Along came a pixie with a penny one day,
Bought a currant bun and took it away.

Four currant buns in a baker's shop,
Shiny and round with a cherry on top.
Along came a dragon with a penny one day,
Bought a currant bun and took it away.

Three currant buns in a baker's shop,
Shiny and round with a cherry on top.
Along came a giant with a penny one day,
Bought a currant bun and took it away.

Two currant buns in a baker's shop,
Shiny and round with a cherry on top.
Along came an elf with a penny one day,
Bought a currant bun and took it away.

One currant bun in a baker's shop,
Shiny and round with a cherry on top.
Along came a goblin with a penny one day,
Bought the currant bun and took it away.

No currant buns in a baker's shop,
Shiny and round with a cherry on top.
Along came a fairy with a penny one day
But all the buns were gone,
                    so she flew right away.

Ten little fingers

I have ten little fingers and they all belong to me.
I can make them do things — would you like to see?
I can shut them up tight, I can open them wide.
I can put them together, I can make them all hide.
I can make them jump high. I can make them jump low.
I can fold them up quietly and hold them just so.

Round and round the garden

Round and round the garden
Like a teddy bear,
One step, two step …
Tickle you under there!

18

Five little leprechauns

Five little leprechauns standing in a row,
Three stood straight
And two stood so,
Along came the General,
And what do you think?
Those two little leprechauns
JUMPed — quick as a wink!

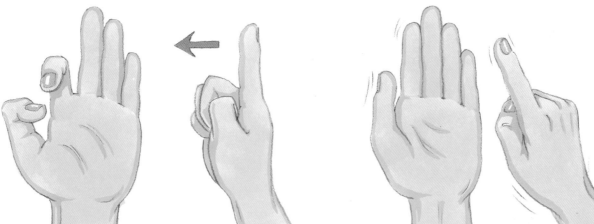

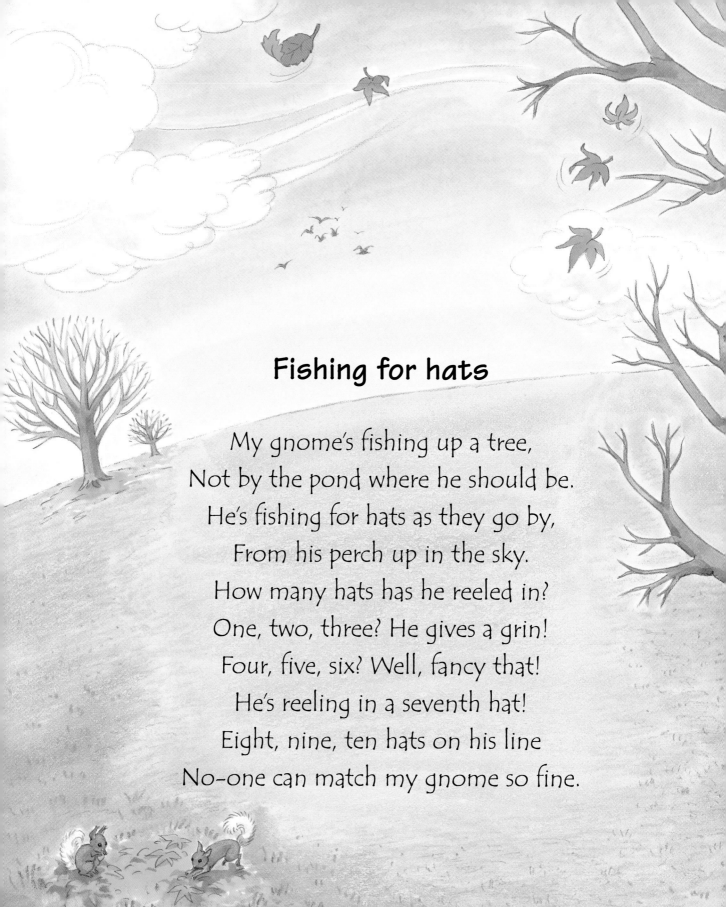

Fishing for hats

My gnome's fishing up a tree,
Not by the pond where he should be.
He's fishing for hats as they go by,
From his perch up in the sky.
How many hats has he reeled in?
One, two, three? He gives a grin!
Four, five, six? Well, fancy that!
He's reeling in a seventh hat!
Eight, nine, ten hats on his line
No-one can match my gnome so fine.

Two little fairies

Two little fairies by a fairy well,
One named Buttercup, one named Belle,

Fly away Buttercup, fly away Belle,
Come back Buttercup, come back Belle.

Puff!

One puff, two puffs, three puffs, four
Five puffs, six puffs –
You can't see me anymore!

I love six pence

I love six pence, a jolly, jolly six pence,
I love six pence as my life;
I spent a penny of it, I spent a penny of it,
I took a penny home to my wife.

I love four pence, a jolly, jolly, four pence,
I love four pence as my life;
I spent two pence of it, I spent two pence of it,
I took two pence home to my wife.

I love nothing, a jolly, jolly nothing,
I love nothing as my life;
I spent nothing of it, I spent nothing of it,
I took nothing home to my wife.

Whistle and I'll come to thee

There were two fairies upon a tree,
Whistle and I'll come to thee;
    Another came, and there were three,
    Whistle and I'll come to thee;
        Another came and there were four,
        You needn't whistle any more,
            For being frightened, off they flew,
            And there are none to show to you.

One for sorrow

One for sorrow,

Two for joy,

Three for a girl,

Four for a boy,

Five for silver,

Six for gold,

Seven for a secret

That is never to be told.

Pixie Trix, Pixie Trix

Pixie Trix, Pixie Trix
Bet you a penny you can't do this:

Number one – touch your tongue

Number two – touch your shoe

Number three – touch your knee

Number four – touch the floor

Number five – jump alive

Number six – do pixie skips

Number seven – cluck like a hen

Number eight – shut the gate

Number nine – remember this rhyme

Number ten – start again.

Five green giants

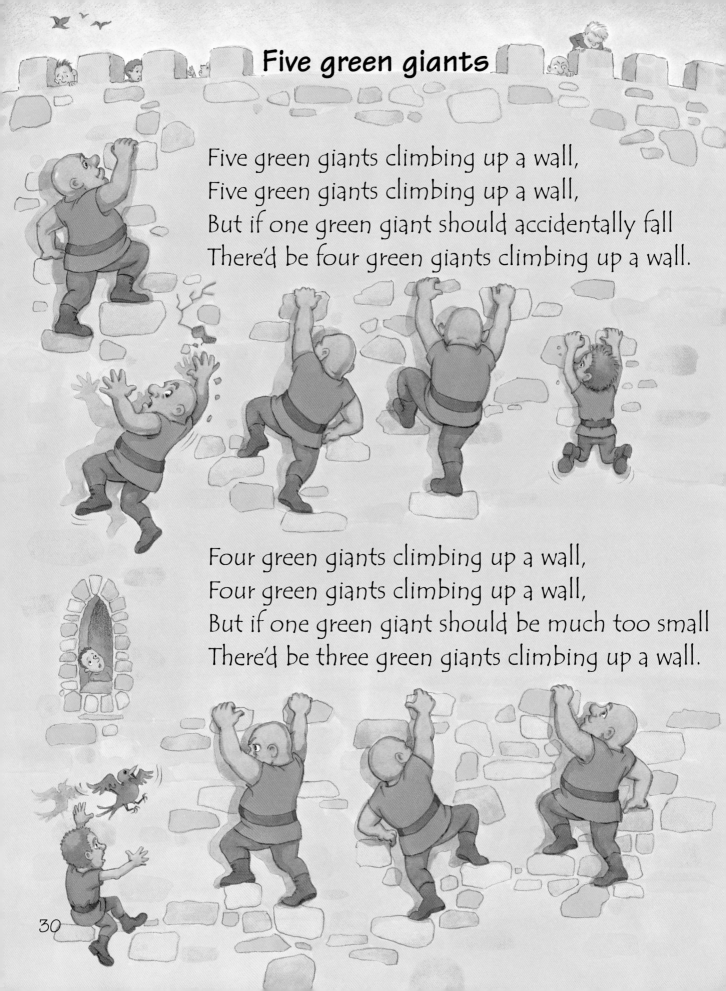

Five green giants climbing up a wall,
Five green giants climbing up a wall,
But if one green giant should accidentally fall
There'd be four green giants climbing up a wall.

Four green giants climbing up a wall,
Four green giants climbing up a wall,
But if one green giant should be much too small
There'd be three green giants climbing up a wall.

Three green giants climbing up a wall,
Three green giants climbing up a wall,
But if one green giant should stop to bounce a ball
There'd be two green giants climbing up a wall.

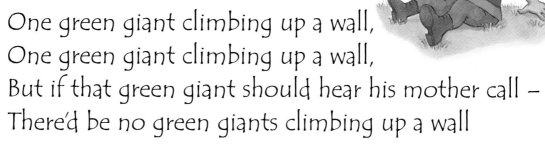

Two green giants climbing up a wall,
Two green giants climbing up a wall,
But if one green giant didn't like to climb at all
There'd be one green giant climbing up a wall.

One green giant climbing up a wall,
One green giant climbing up a wall,
But if that green giant should hear his mother call –
There'd be no green giants climbing up a wall

Three naughty gnomes

Three naughty gnomes with toadstool homes,
Three jolly giants who liked to roam,
Three fickle fairies from sycamore trees,
Three pesky pixies riding bees,
Went outside to take the air,
With smart new clothes and tidy hair,
But suddenly it chanced to rain
And so they all went home again.

One potato, two potato

One potato, two potato,
Three potato, four,
Five potato, six potato,
Seven potato, more!

There were ten in a bed

There were **ten** in a bed
And the little one said,
"Roll over! Roll over!"
So they all rolled over
And one fell out.

There were **nine** in the bed
And the little one said,
"Roll over! Roll over!"
So they all rolled over
And one fell out.

There were **eight** in the bed
And the little one said,
"Roll over! Roll over!"
So they all rolled over
And one fell out.

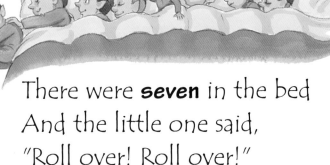

There were **seven** in the bed
And the little one said,
"Roll over! Roll over!"
So they all rolled over
And one fell out.

There were **six** in the bed
And the little one said,
"Roll over! Roll over!"
So they all rolled over
And one fell out.

There were **five** in the bed
And the little one said,
"Roll over! Roll over!"
So they all rolled over
And one fell out.

There were **four** in the bed
And the little one said,
"Roll over! Roll over!"
So they all rolled over
And one fell out.

There were **three** in the bed
And the little one said,
"Roll over! Roll over!"
So they all rolled over
And one fell out.

There were **two** in the bed
And the little one said,
"Roll over! Roll over!"
So they all rolled over
And one fell out.

There was **one** in the bed
And the little one said,
"Roll over! Roll over!"
So they all rolled over
And one fell out.

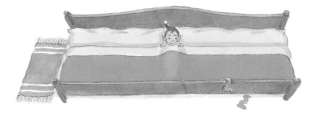

There were **none** in the bed
So no one said,
"Roll over! Roll over!"

35

As I was going to St Ives

As I was going to St Ives,
I met a gnome with seven wives,
Each wife had seven sacks,
Each sack had seven cats,
Each cat had seven kits;
Kits, cats, sacks, and wives,
How many were going to St Ives?

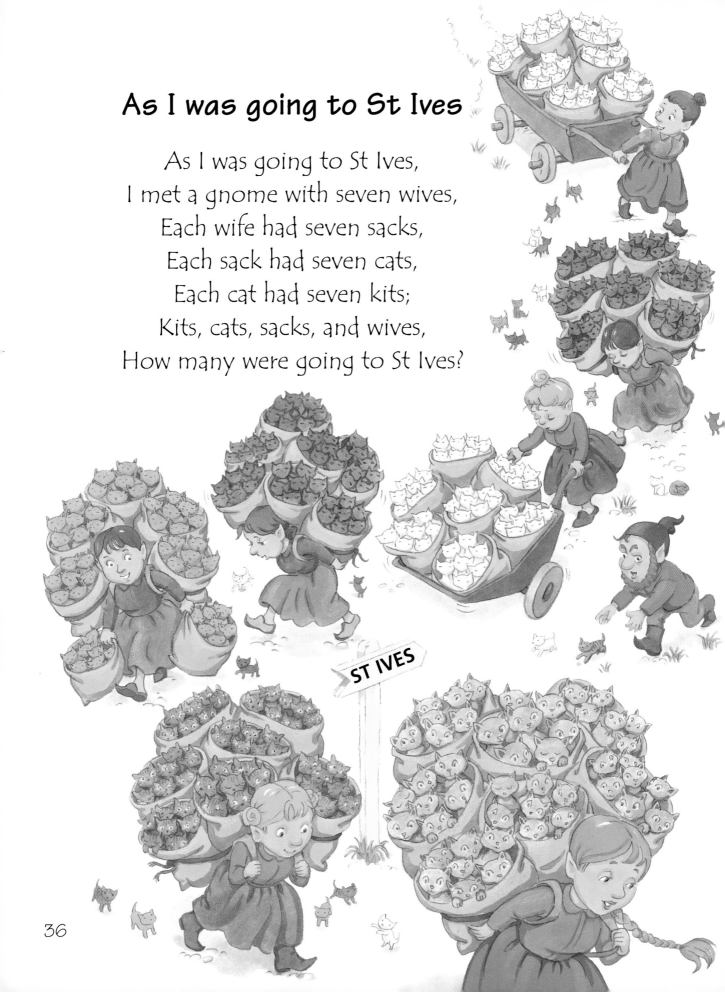

ST IVES

Seven hairy trolls

Seven hairy trolls, sitting back to back,
Fished from the bridge for a pike or a jack.
The first caught a tiddler,
The second caught a crab,
The third caught a winkle,
The fourth caught a dab,
The fifth caught a tadpole,
The sixth caught an eel,
The seventh caught the spokes of an old cart-wheel.

Four giants racing

Get ready, get steady! Go! Go! Go!
Four giants racing, striding in a row.
Mighty Mick's out in front, his bald head bobbing,
And here comes Fiendish Fred, his fat tummy wobbling.

With a fee, and a fi, and a fo-fo-fum,
Four giants racing, see how fast they run.
Bad Bert is closing in, a-pushing and a-shoving,
But Dizzy Dan trips him up, and sends Bert flying.

With a huff, and a puff, and an "Oh! Oh! Oh!"
Four giants racing, now rather slow.
Stumbling, mumbling, moaning in a heap,
They crawl to the finishing line, and fall fast asleep.

One,
two, three, four

One, two, three, four,
Fairy at the cottage door,
Five, six, seven, eight,
Eating cherries off a
plate.

Chook, chook

Chook, chook, chook, chook, chook,
Good morning, Mrs. Hen.
How many chickens have you got?
Madam, I've got ten.
Four of them are yellow,
And four of them are brown,
And two of them are speckled red,
The nicest in the town.

Five giant toes

Five giant toes, wiggling in a sock,
Out goes one, with a great big

POP!

Four giant toes, wiggling in a sock,
Out sneaks one, with a tiny

hop.

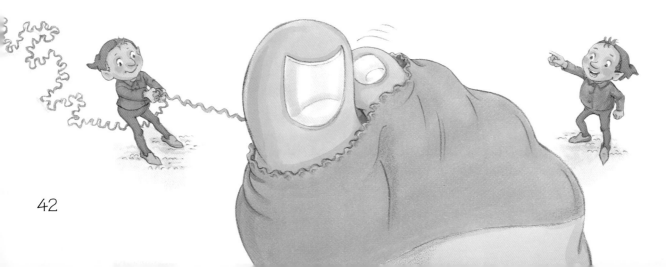

Three giant toes, wiggling in a sock,
Out leaps one, with a lively dance.

Two giant toes, wiggling in a sock,
Out creeps one, without a second glance.

One giant toe, missing all the others,
Wriggles out slowly to join his brothers.

One, two, buckle my shoe

One, two
buckle my shoe;

Three, four
knock at the door;

Five, six
pick up sticks;

Seven, eight
lay them straight;

Nine, ten
a big, fat hen;

Eleven, twelve
dig and delve;

Thirteen, fourteen
maids a-courting;

Fifteen, sixteen
maids in the kitchen;

Seventeen, eighteen
maids in waiting;

Nineteen, twenty
my plate's empty!

45

How many fairies can you see?

How many fairies can you see?
One on the fence, one in the tree
One on your shoulder, one in your hair
And one on the roof, right up there!

How many fairies can you see?
One in my hand, one on my knee
One on the fishpond, one in a rose
And one flying by, right past your nose!

Let's count the fairies, one, two, three
Four buzzing round like tiny bees
But look! Oh no! Just as I feared,
Every little fairy has just …

disappeared!

Index of first lines